The Parable of the Pencil

Philip M. Hudson

This book may be ordered from online bookstores.

Publishing Services by BookCrafters
Parker, Colorado.
www.bookcrafters.net

Table of Contents

Preface

Preface

Unlike an allegory, which is a representation of abstract ideas, a parable is a succinct story set in prose or verse that illustrates principles. It differs from a fable in that the latter employs animals, plants, inanimate objects, or forces of nature, whereas the former has human characters.

The Parable of the Pencil illuminates the principles related to the preservation of family history to strengthen the divine center in each of us. Thereby, our recognition of God's design increases. We are empowered to fulfil our destiny as spiritual beings having mortal experiences. The parable suggests that we need only to listen for, act upon, and record for our edification and that of our posterity, the sweet stirrings that are spiritual promptings.

As my editor suggested after reading the manuscript copy of The Parable of the Pencil, my literary motivation may have been subliminally autobiographical. Her observation helped me to realize that my inspiration to tell this story was indeed personal. The longest journey, she reminded me, is the journey inward, and I now view the parable as an attempt to codify my feelings as I try to find my way home.

As Polonius counsels in Shakespeare's "Hamlet": "This above all, to thine own self be true, and it must follow, as the night the day, thou canst not then be false to any man." (Act 1, Scene 3). The Parable of the Pencil is visceral because it demands that we be honest with ourselves, and acknowledge our imperfections, as we strive for improvement.

The ancient Greek aphorism "know thyself", is one of the Delphic maxims. The two that follow are "nothing to excess" and "surety brings ruin." If these be true, then the tenets of

faith that are embedded within the parable showcase, within the boundaries the Lord has set, the necessity of humility against the backdrop of the immutability of the overarching principles of progress and perfection. (See Matthew 5:48). As the life of the prince unfolds within the parable, we see more clearly that with God all things are possible. (See Matthew 19:26).

As long as He is leading us, guiding us, walking beside us, and helping us find the way, we need only to look in the mirror to find the inspiration we need to live with Him someday. (See Naomi Randall, "I am a Child of God."). Although we may feel that we are taking only baby steps on the pathway to perfection, the parable invites us to be our best, no matter our stage of development. We do this by instinctively drawing upon our intrinsic sense of self-worth that is nothing less than a gift from our Father in Heaven.

The journey of a thousand miles begins with one small step that too few recognize as a leap of faith. As the Virgin Queen was taught: "This much I know. When the storm breaks, each of us must act in accordance with our nature. Initially, some may be dumb with terror. Some may flee, and some may hide, but there will always be those who spread their wings like eagles, and soar on the wind." ("Elizabeth: The Golden Age").

In the parable, the prince discovers a wonderful gift; that each day of our lives is a love letter sent from heaven, to be opened with gratitude. As he learned to do, so must we also pledge to God, angels, and witnesses that the time allotted to us shall be for gain, good, and success, that we might not regret the performance cost we have paid for the precious minutes and hours that are a celestial endowment.

And so, we act in faith, confident that the achievement of our goals is sure to happen. Our deeds reflect our determination to be the kind of individuals our Father in Heaven knows us to be,

vi

and everything we do expresses our resolve to be worthy of His trust, and honor Him.

Those who have studied the dialogue between Edmund Dantès and the priest Abbé Faria, that occurred deep within the walls of the prison of the Chateau d'If, in Alexandere Dumas' novel "The Count of Monte Cristo" will resonate with a recognition of the light that illuminated the soul of the young prince in the parable, even during his darkest and loneliest hours of self-doubt, timidity, hesitation, and indecision.

"What are you thinking?" asked the Abbé. "I was reflecting," replied Dantès, "upon the enormous degree of intelligence and ability you must have employed to reach the high perfection to which you have attained. What would you not have accomplished if you had been free" to do as you wish? "Possibly nothing at all," replied the priest. "The overflow of my brain would probably, in a state of freedom, have evaporated in a thousand follies. Misfortune is needed to bring to light the treasures of the human intellect. Compression is needed to explode gunpowder. Captivity has brought my mental faculties to a focus, and you are well aware that from the collision of clouds electricity is produced, and from electricity, lightning, and from lightning, illumination."

Finally, at the end of the tale, Dantès observes: "Only a man who has despaired is capable of feeling ultimate bliss. It is necessary to have brushed up against the cheek of death, in order to know how good it is to live. Live, then, and be happy, and never forget that, until the day God deigns to reveal the future, the sum of human wisdom will be contained in these words: wait and hope." (See Isaiah 40:31).

Looking at the guiding principles of the parable in this light, and especially in the context of jihad, or the struggle, that was stitched into the experience of the young prince during

his journey of conscience, I have discovered that it is in many ways "the story of us." Truly, none of us is an island; we are in this together, and our interwoven fortunes rise and fall as on the tides. God gives us weaknesses, that we might be humble. Then, by His infinite grace and our abiding faith, He makes weak things become strong unto us. (See Ether 12:27).

Thus, the parable has a cathartic capacity. Its real value may be as the persuasive vehicle of our own expression, by clothing our hopes, and our desires, and our dreams, in word portraits that give substance to the script that we have been asked to memorize in the theater of life. It brings our expectations down out of the stratosphere, by providing real-world perspectives that subtly illuminate eternal principles and energize the pursuit of our realistic goals.

When those who read The Parable of the Pencil apply these principles to greater efforts related to self-improvement, I will have accomplished my objective, that only snapped into focus as I grappled with the creation of its prose. That process exposes my vulnerability, inasmuch as it throws open a window on my soul. But it is also an invitation to join me in my on-going wrestle to understand God's love. (See Genesis 32:34).

You just don't get it, do you?" said Q to Captain Jean Luc Picard, in "Star Trek, The Next Generation." "The trial never ends. We wanted to see if you had the ability to expand your mind and your horizons, and for one brief moment, you did. For one fraction of a second, you were open to options you had never considered. That is the exploration that awaits you. Not mapping stars and studying nebulae, but charting the unknown possibilities of existence." ("All Good Things").

Just so, the prince in our parable discovers all the hidden mysteries of God's kingdom from days of old, and for ages to

x

come, as he learns to appreciate the good pleasure of God's will concerning all things pertaining to His kingdom. (See D&C 76:7).

A round brilliant cut diamond has 58 facets that reflect light. Within over a hundred verses and footnotes, I hope that The Parable of the Pencil will provide enough reflective surfaces to capture your attention. Perhaps it can do even more. I wrote it to invite the Spirit into your heart, to release its capacity to increase the number of foot-candles of heavenly light that illuminate your soul. May it inspire you to ponder how you might nourish the seeds of greatness that flourished in the fertile soil of royal gardens in the Cradle of Civilization. May it show you how to emulate the hero of the story; the young prince; the man who would be king.

It has been said that some of us see things as they are, and ask why, while others see things that never were, and ask why not. Clearly, the future hangs in the balance, waiting only upon our initiative.

Author's Note

As you read The
Parable of the Pencil,
please utilize the more than
110 footnotes that are sprinkled
throughout the text. These elaborate
upon the geography, culture, history,
and the religion of the ancient Near
Eastern world that are the tapestry
upon which the story has been
stitched, and with which
westerners might be
unfamiliar.

Acknowledgements

As I wrote this parable,
it struck me just how heavily I
have relied upon the examples of
those who been my mystical mentors,
my sensible chaperones, my spiritual
guides, my surrogate saviors, my
compassionate critics, and
everything in between.

They have
been my avatars, the very
manifestations of deity in bodily
forms, my na'vi, the visionaries, who
communicate with God on levels to
which I can only aspire, and my
tsaddik, whom I esteem as
intuitive interpreters of
biblical law and
scripture.

They are my
divine teachers incarnate.
They have offered listening ears,
extended open arms, lifted my spirits,
shown me the way, stretched my mind,
reinforced my faith, strengthened my
testimony, helped me to discover
my wings, given immaterial
support, and provided
of their means.

They have emboldened me with words of encouragement, cheered me on with wise counsel, taught me humility, been there to steady me, soothed my troubled soul, stepped in to nurture me, led me to fountains of living water, wet my parched lips with inspired counsel, and bound up my wounds.

They may
or may not
know who they
are, or how they
have influenced
me, but to each
of them, I will
be eternally
grateful.

The Parable of the Pencil

2

Long ago,
in a faraway caliphate[1]
that had been nurtured in the
cradle of civilization, the righteous
sultan who had ruled in the land
passed on to that undiscovered
country from whose bourne
no traveler has ever
returned.[2]

4

The
crown prince who
was his son now held a
lotus blossom[3] and a sceptre,[4]
with which he was wont to grant
favors to mourners who came
to pay their respects to his
late father.

6

The prince
and his family
fasted and prayed,
and they made blood
sacrifice for three days,[5]
so that when their beloved
patriarch left the mountain
peak of Hara[6] and crossed
the Sarat Bridge,[7] he might
join the company of the
god of his fathers as he
traveled the road
to heaven.[8]

8

Not
long thereafter,
the prince received his
inheritance. If the truth
were to be told, he would
have preferred instead to
have his father back, for
they had been close
companions.

10

The
young prince was
shocked to learn that his
father's will specified that
from a vast accumulation of
worldly goods, he was to receive
just one item, a single jewel of
incomprehensible value and
unsurpassed quality whose
celebrated reputation
was undisputed.

The
magnificence
of the dazzling
stone was undisputed.
In every province of
the Persian Empire,[9]
it was know as
"The Eye of the
Tiger."[10]

14

The gem
was of awesome
beauty and stunning
clarity, enough to take
one's breath away, as does
the smouldering heat that
rises from the sands of
the desert at mid
day.[11]

The treasure had been cut
with precision, and then
flawlessly polished to a
luster that rivaled the
stars in the heavens
on a moonless
winter night.

18

The
young prince
knew that his father
had given the bulk of
his estate to orphans, and
the poor, and wayfarers, and
beggars, and for the release
of captives, and he deeply
appreciated the kindness
and the thoughtfulness
that had also been
shown to him.

20

At the same
time, his mourning
heart found comfort in
anticipation that the stone
might be the key to his
independence and to
a care-free life of
happiness and
prosperity.

22

Accordingly,
he inquired of the most
trusted and respected of his
late father's oracles[12], concerning
what he should do to safeguard
the treasure that, over time, he
was sure would increase in
desirability and in value
sevenfold.

24

The wisest of these
counselors took this
opportunity to fulfill a
clandestine assignment
he had been given from
his departed sovereign
shortly before his
passing.

26

In
a voice heavy
with responsibility,
he admonished his
young liege[13] to
give ear to his
counsel.

28

Upon hearing the
whispered instruction
of the oracle, the puzzled
look on the face of the
young prince betrayed
his confusion.

For he had been
urged to make haste,
and to gather only those
provisions he could carry with
him, take the jewel, and ride his
strongest horse at a full gallop to
the great marketplace of a fabled
city in a distant land within the
Fertile Crescent[14] between the
Tigris[15] and the Euphrates[16]
rivers that was known
as Mesopotamia.

The
lad had been
tutored in Sharia
Law,[17] and at an early
age had been taught to
be obedient to both Allah[18]
and his elders. "So let it
be written; so let it be
done!"[19] had become
his motto.

And so, without
hesitation, the youth did as
he had been told. As soon as he
arrived in the metropolis, known
since ancient times as Samarra,[20] in
accordance with the further detailed
instruction that had been provided
by the palace prognosticator,[21] he
searched diligently throughout
all the bazaars.[22]

He
canvassed
every souk,[23] that
he might find an
amenable merchant
who would barter[24]
for the gem.

38

For this
had been his father's
wish via the oracle: to
use the bauble to obtain
the most reliable writing
instrument that could
be found in all of
Persia.

40

The oracle
had been explicit
in his instruction, for
he had dreamed a dream;
that is to say, he had shared a
vision with the old king. He knew
that it was qisma,[25] or kismet,[26]
that there might be found one
merchant in particular who
would eagerly accept the
jewel in a fair trade
with the prince.

But first,
the young heir to the
throne would have to avoid
forty theives[27] who had heard
rumors about his inheritance,
and who were even then
slinking about in the
shadowy alleyways
of the city.

They
were lying
in wait, that
they might slit his
throat and steal the
jewel. As they plotted to
hatch their nefarious plan,
they envisioned leaving
him for dead, that the
ravens might pick
his bones.

46

These
demons, together
with other evil spirits,
were fiendish powers that had
been unleased by the Scythians.[28]
Like locusts,[29] they descended upon
Samarra from the plains of Northern
Asia, sniffing around in search of
clues that would divulge the
location of the fabled
Eye of the Tiger.

But the ideals and
principles that guided the
young prince were uncorrupted,
and his heart was pure. He sought
neither favor nor the attention of
others, he was true to the trust
that had been placed in him,
and he was faithful to the
commission he had
been given.

50

Allah protected
him and, though he
walked in the valley of
the shadow of death[30] on
more than one occasion,
he was delivered from
out of the hands
of evildoers.

He
bore with
equanmity the
stripes that were
given him by a cruel
and unforgiving world,
and hoped that what did
not kill him would make
him stronger.

He felt the protection of
angels sent from heaven, and
the guidance of Zarathustra,[31]
the great prophet of Mazdaism.[32]
With these fortifications, the young
prince was able to surmount every
obstacle that was thrown up in
his pathway to defeat the
purpose of his quest.

He
was about to
learn that sacrifice
requires that we give up
one thing, that we we might
enjoy, in its place, another
thing that proves to be
of greater value.

And
so it came
to pass that
the young prince
parted company with
the legendary Eye of the
Tiger, and found himself,
instead, the possessor of
a splendid cylindrical
device half a cubit[33]
in length.

60

In spite of
its diminutive
size, it would prove,
in time, to be far more
powerful than the cat's
eye that had been
surrendered
in trade.

And
in Samarra
that very night,
there was a happy
merchant who went to
evening prayer to offer
his thanks to Allah for
permitting him to have
been of service to the
young caliph.[34] To be
sure, he cried out,
Allahu akbar.[35]

64

As
soon as the
young prince
had a chance to
thoroughly examine
his new possession, he
noticed that it was of
curious workmanship,
with a shiny surface
that was above the
color of the sun
at noonday.

At one end was a
diaphanous[36] pool of
graphite that had been
sharpened to a point that
rivaled the cutting edge
of the Damascus blade[37]
the prince carried
on his sash.[38]

The
other end
was blunted by
an intriguingly soft
but delightfully spongy
pink compound that, he had
been reassured, would flawlessly
absorb and then magically render
invisible, every trace of errors in
penmanship that might be made
by the one who guided the
path of the instrument
across parchment.

This, the
merchant had
promised him, might
be accomplished without
so much as the utterance of
"Abracadabra"[39] even if the
incantation were twice
repeated.

72

The
plaintive cry
of the muezzin[40]
calling the faithful
to evening prayer[41] was
still ringing in his ears as
the prince carefully wrapped
his purchase in fine silks
and precious linens.[42]

These exotic wares
had been obtained from
nomadic travelers who had only
recently arrived from shadowy and
distant Cathay,[43] over the time-worn
trading route that followed the Qaryat
al-fau,[44] the Incense Trail, through a
corridor in the Tuwaiq Mountains[45]
along the northwest edge of the
Rub' al Khali,[46] or the Empty
Quarter of the Arabian
Peninsula.

As he
set out on his
homeward journey,
for reasons of safety,
he went by way of an
alternate route that
carried him along
the Frankincense
Trail.[47]

78

That sure
path carried him
to the sanctuary of his
faith, where he took great
comfort in the wisdom and
judgment of his late father's
most trusted advisor.

80

He was
confronted by many
worldly enticements that
clamored for his undivided
attention, but he was resolute,
unyielding, and determined
to return with honor. Thus,
his long journey home
became a rite of
passage.[48]

82

He knew that
Allah would neither
abandon him nor allow
him to be tempted beyond
his capacity to resist evil,
and so he plodded on,
with a silent prayer
of thanksgiving
in his heart.

84

He looked neither
to the right nor to the
left,[49] and in his mind's eye, he
could see date palms flourishing
amidst the refreshsing oases of his
native land, inviting him to freely
partake[50] of their bounty, and
to drink deeply from the
flowing undercurrents
of living waters.[51]

As the seven deadly
sins of pride, greed, wrath,
envy, lust, gluttony, and sloth[52]
continued to probe his senses, he
met them squarely, with clear eyes
and with a conscience that was
void of offense toward any
man, or Allah.[53]

As he faced
these temptations,
he did not need to
remind himself that
he was the son
of a king.[54]

90

He was continualy
fortified by the heavenly
virtues that he had embraced in
his father's household. These were
the merits of prudence, justice,
temperance, and courage,
as well as faith, hope,
and charity.[55]

Not on tables of
stone, but instead upon the
fleshy tables of his own heart,[56]
these virtues had been indelibly
imprinted, empowering him to
embrace impossible dreams,
to fight unbeatable foes,
to shoulder unbearable
sorrow, and to run
where the brave
dare not go.[57a]

His life
choices had
prepared him "to
amend the unrightable
wrong, to love pure and
chaste from afar, to try,
when his arms felt too
weary, and to reach
the unreachable
star."57b

96

He would now
follow that beacon
of light, no matter how far
his quest might take him, or
for how long he must persevere.
He was eager and willing to fight
for the right without question or
pause; even if that meant he
"must march into hell for
a heavenly cause."[57c]

He determined
be true to the faith of his
fathers, that his heart, too, might
lie peaceful and calm when he was
laid to his rest. He did not know what
the future would bring, but he did know
this: that, although he be scorned and
covered with scars, he would strive
with his last ounce of courage "to
reach the unreachable star."[57d]

100

For this much
he knew: that no-one
could rob him of the sure
knowledge that he had honored
the wishes of his father,[58] and had
followed the instructions of the
oracle to the last letter of the
abjad,[59] the Arabic alphabet
he had been taught
in his youth.

102

And so, he
traveled on for
four days and three
nights, reflecting upon
the possibility that his new
possession, called a "pencil"
by the merchant with whom
he had negotiated the trade
of the jewel, might be of
great worth, but he did
not know why this
would be so.

He did not
yet recognize
his acquisition
as the formidable
treasure that would,
over time, become the
authoritative vehicle
of his personal
expression.

106

For he had not
yet been sufficiently
instructed by Allah, that the
pencil might become the means
of his liberation from a life that
would be threatened by mediocrity,
by repetitively wearisome learning
experiences, frustrating failure,
and even by unrecognized
or uncelebrated
success.

Nevertheless,
upon his return to the
familiar surrounding of
the palace that was his
home, he guarded the
pencil on his person
at all times, even
sleeping with it
at his side.

For there
were, as yet,
forces within his
own kingdom, that
would influence him
to abandon his ideals,
forsake true principles,
and yield to the baser
instincts of human
nature.

Even in
the midst of these
challenges, however, not
once did the counselor
in the court of his late
father reveal to him
the power of the
pencil.

Instead, in
answer to his
persistent inquiries,
the young prince was
repeatedly counseled that
he must discover for
himself its true
value.

The Spirit
would lead him,
guide him, and walk
beside him, showing him
the way to enlightenment.[60]
If the young prince would
allow Him to, Allah would
touch the eyes of his
understanding.

118

He would
reveal great and
marvelous things to
the young prince, even
mysteries that had been
withheld and kept secret
from the minds of men
since the creation
of the world.

As
time passed,
the fig trees[61] in the
royal orchards matured,
and the grape vines[62] in
the royal vineyards
bore abundant
fruit.

The
olive trees[63]
growing in the royal
gardens blossomed each
spring, and became heavily
laden by early summer. At
harvest time, the presses
produced more talents[64]
of oil than any other
grove within the
caliphate.

So too,
with the passing
years, did the young
prince grow, both
in wisdom and
in stature.

126

On lazy
afternoons in
the palace gardens,
he had dreams, and in
the darkest hours before
the dawn, as he lay in his
apartments, he experienced
visions, and at sundry times
and in diverse places,[65] he
became the recipient of
intensely personal
revelations.

128

As he
slumbered
upon his bed and
when deep sleep fell
upon him, he closed his
eyes, and it was only then
that Allah opened his
ears, and sealed his
instruction.[66]

130

When sweet
inspiration flowed
to his mind as from a jar
of honey,[67] he learned to retrieve
from its place of safe-keeping the
instrument, in order to record his
impressions in the venerable
Achaemenid[68] language
of his ancestors.

132

As the
young prince
learned to accept
the guidance of Allah,
the power of the pencil
was strong,[69] so much so
that he could feel it as it
coursed through his body,
and most importantly,
as it touched his
heart.

Each
morning, he
would remember
that God is great,
and in his prayers,
he would consecrate
his energy to Him Who
holds the destiny of
men, women, and
nations in His
omnipotent
hands.

136

As a
result of his daily
devotions, he began to
understand that whisperings
both inarticulate and intangible
could influence him for good, if
he would but preserve in writing
the prompting that he had so
powerfully received.

138

When
he heard
the howling
wind blowing off
the desert, he came to
appreciate that he could
not tell from whence it had
come, or where it might go.[70]
It was the pencil, he realized,
that would help establish the
orientation of his spiritual
compass, as well as to
maintain its proper
calibration.[71]

As he
employed
the pencil to
record his spiritual
experiences, He came
to understand how it
could help him as he
called upon Allah
when he sensed
that He was
near.[72]

142

With
maturity, he
became an astute
judge of human nature,
and a perceptive observer of
the dramas that continually
unfolded before him in the
splendid courtyards
of the palace.

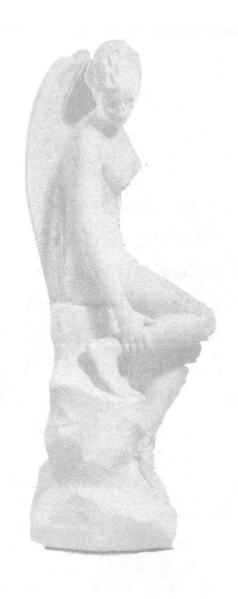

144

He began
to rely upon the
pencil as a valuable
tool to document the
more significant of
these intriguing
interactions.

146

Over time,
as he learned to
deal with adversity in
the theater of life, the
journals he had created
became of immeasurable
value, and he turned to
them again and again,
that his trials might
be put in proper
perspective.

148

His were the same challenges with which all mortals, not only princes but also paupers, the wise as well as the foolish, and the high and the mighty as well as the lowly of heart, must inevitably and individually grapple.

150

Fortunately, his late
father had taught him to listen
attentively to his subjects, for they
were as a well of water, the flowing
source of all manner of information
that pertained to the quality of the
affairs of state in every far-flung
province of the kingdom.

152

Whenever the
maturing sovereign
learned of compliments
or criticisms that related to
the administration of justice
within his realm, he recorded
the same with the instrument
of writing that, in time, he
came to regard as his
greatest temporal
possession.

154

It was
truly a pearl
of great price[73]
more to be desired
than gold, and more
precious than rubies, or
the diamond, the beryl,
the jasper, or the onyx,
emerald, the sapphire,
or the carbuncle.[74]

156

With
the passing
years, the pencil
helped the prince to
become a wellspring of
wisdom that he generously
shared with others. He married
well, and sired many offspring.
The halls of the palace were
filled with the music of
the laughter of
children.

His
children grew all
too fast, but he never
missed the opportunity
to utilize the object of his
inheritance to document what
came to be known, not only
in his own household, but
also among his subjects,
as his family history.[75]

He
inclined his
ear to wisdom
and applied his heart
to understanding.[76] The
fame of his erudition spread
far and wide, even to the
kingdom of Saba[77] where
the Queen of Sheba[78]
marveled at his
insight.

Wherever he
went, from the Statue
of Zeus at Olympia to the
Pyramids of Giza, from the
Mausoleum at Halicarnassus to the
Hanging Gardens of Babylon, from the
Lighthouse of Alexandria to the Colossus
of Rhodes and the Temple of Artemis
at Ephesus, the reputation of the
prince preceded him.[79]

Even on
pilgrimmages to
the Al-Aqsa Mosque[80] in
Jerusalem,[81] because his book
of remembrance had been widely
distributed and studied throughout
the kingdom, the name of the prince
was prominently conspicuous in
conversations around the
evening campfires.

In the sacred
precincts of the Kaaba[82]
in Mecca,[83] his name was
included among those of
the messengers of Islam[84]
that were whispered with
deferential approbation
in the prayers of
the faithful.

At the
prophet's Mosque[85] in
Medina,[86] when entreaties
were made to the angels for
their intercession,[87] the prince
was petitioned as well, for
his benevolence and his
compassion were well
established.

Woven into the
tapestry of his recorded
experiences that contributed to
the growing mystique associated
with his reign, were the impressions
that he continually received, as he
increasingly relied upon guidance
from the unseen world. These,
he was wont to describe in
his expanding chronicle
as "the whisperings of
the Spirit."[82]

He once
confided to
his privy council
that, were it not for
his precious instrument
of writing, he, his family,
and his subjects would have
benefitted but for a moment
from the inspiration he had
received.[89] It would have
evaporated as does the
gentle mist of rainfall
on desert wastes.[90]

174

Particulary in
times of trial, when the
wind of adversity blew its
hardest, and the sandstorms
of life[91] threatened to suck the
breath from his lungs, he clung
to his faith, as well as to that
which he had written, that
he came to regard as
personal scripture.

The
years slipped by
almost unawares, one
by one, and he could sense
that his memory was beginning
to fade. He knew that were it not
for his pencil, the framework upon
which his relationships with others
had been constructed would have
disintegrated in the mercurial
mist of time.[92]

Were it not
for his pencil,
the lives of those
within the sphere of his
influence might have been
superficially touched, but they
certainly would not have been
profoundly transformed, and
his eternal destiny, let alone
that of his precious family,
would have hung in
the balance.

180

Instead, because
he had been faithful
to utilize the pencil every
day of his life, the sum of his
experiences had been preserved,
according to the rationality of
Islam[93] that the Prophet[94] had
described so well in his
holy text.

182

With
modesty that was
befitting a monarch who
understood the responsibility
of stewardship, in his petitions
to Allah, he acknowledged the
part the pencil had played in
his efforts to preserve for
many generations his
family's pedigree.

184

Thru
the power
of the written
word, his life's
story would now
have substance and
meaning for countless
of his loved ones, even
for those yet unborn, and
it would be eagerly shared
on both sides of the veil.

186

All this, he
gratefully realized
as he gazed upon the bright
countenances of his wife, sons,
daughters, and grandchildren, was
because he had heeded the wise
counsel of a trusted advisor
who could see beyond the
impetuosity of his
youth.

188

The prince
had first trusted,
and had then followed
without a moment's hesitation,
the guidance of his elder, to sell his
inheritance, so that he might possess the
means to record his impressions of that
which would influence both him and
his loved ones for good, during
the course of lives that he
hoped would prove to
be well-lived.

190

Without question,
he had acted upon the
instruction to sell what he
had initially thought to be a
noteworthy inheritance, but that
proved to be nothing more than a
pretty pebble, or a telestial trinket.
He had not yet grasped that the
significance of the Eye of the
Tiger was as sounding
brass and tinkling
cymbals.[95]

The
oracle had
looked beyond
the horizon of the
young prince's vision,
and saw his future as an
ever-present reality; not as
something that could be,
but as something that
must be so.[96]

Time waits
for no man,[97] be he
of noble or of humble
birth, and so it was in the
case of him who had begun
his journey of self-discovery as
an inexperienced youth, but who
embraced his date with destiny as
a faithful son, a beloved husband,
a perceptive father, and finally
as an experienced elder
statesman.

He had become a true
patriarch in the likeness and
image of his progenitor through
a miracle that was nothing
less than a spiritual
transformation.

Within his
heart, he had
learned how to
love. But more than
that, he had discovered
how to live, that he might
enjoy not only the blinding
rays of the sun, but also
the soft glow of
moonlight.[98]

200

He
had come
to know peace,
as well as plenty.
But more importantly,
he had learned this life
lesson: We can never get
enough of what we don't
need, because it will
never satisfy
us.

202

With his last
breath, He sought to
reassure and comfort his
loved ones: "Think not that I
dread to see my spirit fly thru
the dark gates of mortality.
Death holds no terror when
life has been true. It is
living ill that makes
us fear to die."[99]

204

In the springtime
of the year and on the
evening of a full moon,
he passed away peacefully,
surrounded by his family
and with a smile on
his countenance.

206

He had only recently
recorded before witnesses his
declaration of faith, as well as his
Last Will and Testament,[100] utilizing the
same instrument of writing that had
proven to be a trusted traveling
companion throughout his
long and productive
life.

208

No-one
was surprised,
when it was published
throughout the kingdom
after his passing, that he had
observed zakat[101] as one of
the five immovable pillars
of his religion.[102]

These had
encompassed duty
to Allah, to personal
spiritual growth, and a
commitment to care for
the poor, as well as to be
self-disciplined, and to
become accustomed
to sacrifice.

The greatest
bulk of his earthly
estate had been left to
a number of charitable
organizations, for the
benefit of the poor
and the needy.[103]

214

At his
funeral, the
Sufi poet Jalal
al Din Muhammad
Rumi[104] eulogized
the prince. "When we
are dead," he said,
"seek not our tomb
in the earth, but
find it in the
hearts of
men."

216

None
of his subjects
were shocked when
it was revealed that the
most trusted and respected
of his oracles had been charged
with the responsibility to see that
each one of his children received
as their inheritance at the bequest
of their father, a single jewel of
unsurpassed quality, immense
value, and celebrated
reputation.

For he, who had
been an inexperienced
young prince, had grown into
a wise and loving father. He was
a venerable and respected Sultan ul
Mujahid,[105] and his introspective jihad[106]
had defined his life and had brought
enlightenment to his kingdom.

220

He had
set both his
temporal and
his spiritual affairs
in order, mustering the
strength in his final days to
issue, with the steady stroke of
his pencil, one last earthly decree,
for he was always thinking of
the welfare of his family.

At
his command,
the Arabian horses[107]
in the royal stables had
been fed the sweetest oats
in the land. Their hooves had
been shod and they had been
groomed and saddled by the
royal blacksmith and stable
boy, and they had been
well-watered at the
pool of Shifa'.[108]

224

They had
been readied,
that they might
carry his children
on only a moment's
notice and as on the
west wind,[109] all the
way to Samarra.

There, in
the bustling marketplace
of that ancient city, a wrinkled,
wizened, and well-regarded, not to
mention temporally wealthy, merchant
would be waiting in hopeful anticipation,
with a fistful of pencils in his tight
grasp, and a twinkle in his eye.
He would be thinking: Surely,
God is Great!

228

Epilogue

230

And
what of the
children? What
did the future
hold in store
for them?

232

عاشو فى تبات و نبات

Wa ashu fe hanna'a wa sa'ada

They lived peacefully and in bliss.[110]

234

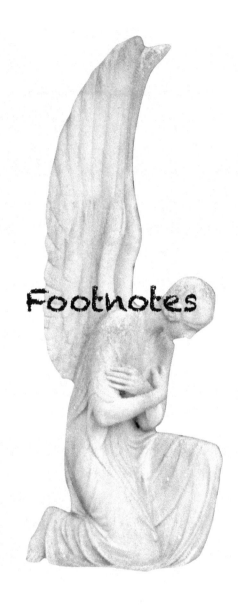

Footnotes

236

Footnotes

1. A caliphate is an Islamic state under the leadership of an individual with the title of caliph, who is considered to be a successor of Mohammed. He governs an ummah, or a community of believers.

2. This phrase is similar to Hamlet's soliloquy, when he muses to no-one in particular, but perhaps to Ophelia: "The undiscovered country from whose bourn no traveler returns, puzzles the will and makes us rather bear those ills we have, than fly to others that we know not of." (Shakespeare, "Hamlet," Act 3, Scene 1).

3. In ancient Zoroastrian fables, both birth and water were born of a lotus blossom. The lotus, or niloofar-e abi, is a symbol of spiritual growth. In an impressive contrast, the flower often grows in swamp land, while turning its petals to the sun. The lotus is an example of how we can look up for redemption, even when we find ourselves in the most pitiable circumstances.

4. The sceptre was central to Mesopotamian life and was part of the royal insignia. It was an emblem of authority, of both sovereigns and the gods.

In the First Persian Empire, the Bible mentions the sceptre of the King of Persia. "When the king saw Esther the queen standing in the court, she obtained favor in his sight; and the king held out to Esther the golden scepter that was in his hand. So Esther came near, and touched the top of the scepter." (Esther 5:2).

5. Early Persia was influenced by Babylonian, Sumerian, and Assyrian funerary practices. All had a basic belief that for three days following death, the spirit walked the earth, before going to the underworld. Therefore, the family of the deceased would offer prayers and animal sacrifices to help their departed loved

ones ward off evil spirits. After descending into the underworld, the only help that could be given to spirits was through repetitive offerings.

Today, Islamic funerals follow fairly specific customs, although they are not spelled out in the Koran. Sharia calls for the burial of the body quickly, usually within 24 hours, preceded by ritual bathing and shrouding, and followed by prayer. Cremation is forbidden in Islam.

6. Sacred mountains are central to many religions, probably because their peaks are believed to be the closest to heaven. The mountains of the Hindu Kush are spurs of the High Hara, which the faithful believe to the geographic center of the universe.

7. According to Islam, in order to enter Paradise, every person must pass over the As-Sirar, or the Sarat Bridge. It is said that it is as thin as a hair, and as sharp as a scimitar. Below the bridge, the fires of hell burn sinners, which makes them fall.

8. Whoever says "Subhan Allah al-Adthim wa Bihamdihi" (Glorified and Exalted is Allah, The Great, and with His Praise), a date-palm tree will planted for him in Jannah, or Paradise.

9. Anciently, Persia was known as the Achaemenid Empire. (559 B.C.E. to 331 B.C.E.) It was larger than any previous empire in history, and was ultimately conquered by Alexander the Great.

The dynasty drew its name from Achaemenes, who, from 705-675 B.C.E. ruled Persia, bounded on the west by the Tigris River and on the south by the Persian Gulf.

Today, we think of the Persian Empire, or Imperial Iran, as any one of the many dynasties centered in Iran from the 6th century B.C.E., (the Achaemenid Empire), to the 20th century C.E., (the Pahlavi dynasty).

240

10. In a literal sense, the Eye of the Tiger refers to the white spot on the back of the tiger's ear. When a tiger goes for the kill, it turns its ears backward, showing the spot, i.e. "the tiger's eyes." If you see these, you are, for all practical purposes, already dead.

"Tigers eye" is also a planetary stone (a form of quartz) for Gemini. Folklore says that wearing tiger's eye is beneficial for health and spiritual well-being, is a psychic protector, and is an aid in achieving clarity of mind.

11. The Rub' al Khali (the Empty Quarter) is the sand desert encompassing most of the southern third of the Arabian Peninsula. Its terrain is covered with dunes as high as 250 meters (820 feet). The region is classified as hyper-arid, with annual precipitation generally less than 35 millimeters (1.4 inches). Daily maximum temperatures average 47° C (117° F) in July and August, reaching peaks of 51° C (124° F).

12. An oracle is a priest through whom the gods communicate through prophecy, divine commands, or with advice that is often allegorical. An oracle may also be a person who is considered to be a source of wisdom.

13. A liege is a feudal lord, who is entitled to the allegiance and service of his subjects.

14. The Fertile Crescent is a region in the Middle East that spans modern-day Iraq, Syria, Lebanon, Israel, Palestine, Jordan, and parts of Egypt, Turkey, and Iran. It has been called "the cradle of civilization," because it is where agriculture was first practiced. The Sumerians flourished in Mesopotamia, (the land between the rivers), inventing irrigation, writing, the wheel, and glass, in the process.

15. The Tigris River is the eastern of the two great rivers that

define Mesopotamia, the other being the Euphrates River. It flows south from the mountains of southeastern Turkey, through Iraq, and empties into the Persian Gulf.

Together with the Euphrates, it is a major river system of western Asia. The region has historical significance as part of the Fertile Crescent.

16. The Euphrates River is the longest and one of the most historically important rivers of Western Asia. Together with the Tigris River, it is one of the two defining rivers of Mesopotamia. It joins the Tigris River in the Shatt al-Arab.

17. Sharia is the totality of God's commands and exhortations, that is intended to regulate all aspects of conduct, and to guide believers on the path of eternal salvation. At various times, God calls prophets to reveal Sharia to mankind. Muslims believe that Mohammed was the last of these messengers to be sent, through whom God revealed the most perfect and complete version of Sharia.

The sources of Sharia are the Koran and the Hadith. Muslims believe the Koran is the collection of the literal words of God transmitted to the prophet Mohammed through the Angel Gabriel. The Koran consist of more than 6,000 verses that were collected shortly after the death of Mohammed in 632 C.E. It is organized into 114 chapters in a single book, which is accepted by all Muslims as the authentic Holy Book of the religion. The Hadith is the collection of the Sunna, or the traditions of Mohammed.

18. Allah is the Arabic word for God, in Abrahamic religions.

19. "So let it be written, so let it be done," are the words of Pharaoh Rameses I, popularized in the Cecil B. DeMille motion picture "The Ten Commandments." The biblical counterpart of the

244

phrase is found in the Book of Matthew: Suffer it to be so now: for thus it becometh us to fulfil all righteousness." (Matthew 3:15).

20. Samarra dates to 5,500 B.C.E. and stands on the east bank of the Tigris River. In medieval times, it was the capital of the Abbasid Caliphate, and is today the only remaining Islamic capital that retains its original plan, architecture, and artistic relics. UNESCO has named Samarra as a World Heritage Site.

21. A prognosticator is one who predicts, or foretells, something. Prognostication is a foreshadowing, or portent, of the future.

22. A bazaar is a permanently enclosed marketplace where merchants, bankers, and craftsmen exchange or sell goods and services.

23. A souk, or souq, is a marketplace, or the commercial quarter, in Western Asian and North African cities.

24 In trade, barter is a system where participants in a transaction swap goods or services without using a medium of exchange, such as money.

25. Qisma is the Arabic term for fate.

26. Kismet means fate, destiny, predestination, or pre-determination by God or some inexplicable force of nature. In Islam, kismet refers to the will of Allah. But it is popularly used to refer to something that one believes is "meant to be," or it is the reason why such a thing happens.

27. Forty thieves figure prominently in "1001 Arabian Nights: Ali Baba and The Forty Thieves." The command: "Open Sesame!" probably needs no explanation.

28. The Scythians were the most dangerous neighbors of Persia. They worshipped their deity under the symbol of a serpent, and it was that snake, Afrasiâb, who became the god of the enemy, identified with the archfiend Ahriman.

29. A large swarm of locusts can consist of billions of insects spread out over an area of thousands of square kilometers, with a population of up to 80 million per square kilometer (200 million per square mile).

30. "Yea, though I walk through the valley of the shadow of death, I will fear no evil, for thou art with me. Thy rod and thy staff they comfort me." (Psalms 23:4).

31. A major figure in the history of world religions, Zarathustra, who lived somewhere between 1,200 and 600 B.C.E., developed the concept of one god, whom he referred to as Ahura Mazda, or the Wise Lord. He also promoted dualism, with a sharp distinction between the forces of good and evil. His teachings influenced emerging Middle Eastern religions, such as Judaism.

32. Zoroastrianism or Mazdayasna is one of the world's oldest continuously practiced religions. It is centered on the dualistic cosmology of good and evil and predicts the ultimate conquest of the latter by a monotheistic god.

33. The cubit is an ancient measurement of length that had several definitions according to each of the various cultures that used it. It was typically around 17 inches.

34. A Caliph is a successor of Mohammed, who was the temporal and spiritual leader of Islam.

35. Allahu Akbar is a common phrase used by Muslims, including the Salah, the obligatory prayers that are recited five times a day. Today, it is widely associated with Muslims who shout it

248

as a slogan, while engaged in jihad, or holy war. Its literal translation is: "God is greater!"

36. Something that is diaphanous is sufficiently thin or airy to permit the passage of light. It is of such a delicate composition that it can be easily damaged or broken.

37. Damascus steel was smithed in the Near East from ingots imported from Southern India and Sri Lanka. Damascus blades are characterized by distinctive patterns of banding and mottling reminiscent of flowing water, in a ladder or teardrop pattern. Aside from its esthetic appeal, Damascus steel was valued because it maintained a keen edge, yet it was hard and flexible. Weapons made from Damascus steel were vastly superior to iron weapons.

38. The sash or girdle was a pleasing style of clothing among the ancients. It was wound several times around the waist to bind the other articles of clothing together.

39. Abracadabra is an incantation, and is probably the best known of all the ancient magical words, or angelic talismans, created in biblical times for the benefit of humanity, by the Magi. Its ability to summon celestial beings of light known as angels was legendary.

However, the Puritan minister Increase Mather dismissed the word as bereft of power, and Daniel Defoe wrote dismissively about Londoners who posted the word on their doorways to ward off sickness during the Great Plague of London (1665 C.E.).

40. The muezzin is the person who has been appointed to lead and recite the call to prayer by the faithful, in a mosque.

41. The Maghrib prayer is one of the five mandatory salah (daily

250

obligatory standardized prayers) in the Islamic religion. It is offered just after the sun goes down. As an Islamic day starts at sunset, the Maghrib prayer is technically the first prayer of the day.

42. Upper classes of ancient Persian society wore fine muslin and imported silk fabrics, while commoners wore locally made and coarse fabrics such as cotton, flax, wool, and leather.

43. Cathay is a historical name for China. In time, it became a poetic name for the nation.

44. The Incense Road included a network of major ancient land and sea trading routes linking the Mediterranean world with eastern and southern sources of incense, spices, and other luxury goods. It wound its way through Northeastern Africa and Arabia to India, and beyond.

45. Jabal Tuwaiq is a narrow geographical escarpment that cuts through the plateau of central Arabia, near the Empty Quarter. Many narrow valleys, or wadis, run through it.

46. The Rub' al Khal, or The Empty Quarter, is the sand desert encompassing most of the southern third of the Arabian Peninsula. It covers parts of Saudi Arabia, Oman, the United Arab Emirates, and Yemen. It is part of the larger Arabian Desert.

47. The Frankincense Trail was a caravan trade route linking present-day Oman, Yemen, and Somalia with markets in the Fertile Crescent and ancient Mesopotamia.

48. A rite of passage describes the process whereby an individual leaves one group to identify with, or associate with, another group.

49. "I will go before your face. I will be on your right hand and on your left, and my Spirit shall be in your hearts, and mine angels round about you, to bear you up." (D&C 84:88, see D&C 49:27).

50. "Every one that thirsteth, come ye to the waters, and he that hath no money; come ye, buy, and eat; yea, come, buy wine and milk without money and without price." (Isaiah 55:1).

51. "For the Lamb which is in the midst of the throne shall feed them, and shall lead them unto living fountains of waters, and God shall wipe away all tears from their eyes." (Revelation 7:17).

52. The seven deadly sins, also known as the capital vices or cardinal sins, is a grouping of vices within Christian teachings, although it does not appear explicitly in the Bible. Behaviors or habits are classified under this category if they directly give birth to other immoralities. According to the standard list, they are pride, greed, wrath, envy, lust, gluttony, and sloth, which are also contrary to the seven heavenly virtues. (See footnote #55).

53. "And herein do I exercise myself, to have always a conscience void of offence toward God, and toward men." (Acts 24:16).

54. In France in the Middle Ages, the heir to the throne was known as the Dauphin. In the reign of King Louis, unscrupulous and crafty counselors tried every means to corrupt the Dauphin, and to thereby render him incapable of inheriting the throne. In all their attempts, they were unsuccessful. Finally, in resignation, they asked him, "How is it that with all our enticements we were unable to compromise your high standards?" His reply was simple, "I am a King's son."

55. Virtue is a habitual and firm disposition to do the good. The seven Christian virtues or heavenly virtues combine the four classical cardinal virtues of prudence, justice, temperance, and

254

courage with the three theological virtues of faith, hope, and charity. These were adopted by the Church Fathers as the seven virtues.

56. "Ye are manifestly declared to be the epistle of Christ ministered by us, written not with ink, but with the Spirit of the living God; not in tables of stone, but in fleshy tables of the heart." (2 Corinthans 3:3).

57a – 57d. Joe Darion wrote the lyrics to "The Impossible Dream," in the musical production "Man of La Mancha."

58. "Honor thy father and thy mother." (Matthew 19:19).

59. An abjad is a type of writing system in which each symbol stands for a consonant, leaving readers to infer the appropriate vowels. The name "abjad" is derived from pronouncing the first letters of the Arabic alphabet in their original order.

60. For nearly 1,600 years, Muslims have understood Islam as the path to enlightenment, that has rescued humanity from ignorance.

61. The fig originated in Asia Minor. References to it appear repeatedly in both the Old and New Testament of the Bible. Some scholars believe the forbidden fruit picked by Eve was a fig rather than an apple. Sumerian stone tablets dating back to 2,500 B.C.E. record culinary use of figs, and remains of fig trees have been found in excavations of Neolithic sites from 5,000 B.C.E. Some historians consider it the first domesticated crop.

Figs hold a position of symbolism in many world religions, including Christianity, Islam, Hinduism, Judaism and Buddhism, representing fertility, peace, and prosperity. Ancient Olympians earned figs for their athletic prowess, and Pliny the Elder extolled the fruit's restorative powers. The prophet Mohammed

256

identified the fig as the one fruit he would most wish to see in Paradise.

62. In the "Odyssey," by Homer, Ulysses says: "The wine urges me on, the bewitching wine, which sets even a wise man to singing and to laughing, and rouses him up to dance and brings forth words which were better left unspoken."

Wine was a reliable drink when the purity of the water supply was questionable. Water even became a symbol of falseness and lies, as noted by Othello: "She was false as water." (Shakespeare, "Othello," Act 5, Scene 2).

The earliest known cultivation of domesticated grapes occurred in what is now Georgia in the Caucasus region of Eurasia, about 6,000 B.C.E. By 4,000 B.C.E., winemaking extended through the Fertile Crescent to the Nile Delta, and to Asia Minor.

63. Olives and olive oil were not only an important part of the ancient Mediterranean diet but also one of the most successful industries in antiquity. Cultivation of the olive spread with Phoenician and Greek colonization from Asia Minor to Iberia and North Africa, and fine olive oil became a valuable trading commodity. The olive also came to have a wider cultural significance, most famously as a branch of peace and as the victor's crown in the ancient Olympiad.

64. The talent was a unit of weight that was introduced in Mesopotamia at the end of the 4th millennium B.C.E. It was divided into 60 minas, each of which was subdivided into 60 shekels. The talent was the largest biblical unit of measurement for weight, equal to about 75 pounds.

65. "And it shall come to pass afterward, that I will pour out my spirit upon all flesh; and your sons and your daughters shall

prophesy, your old men shall dream dreams, your young men shall see visions." (Joel 2:28).

66. "For God speaketh once, yea twice, yet man perceiveth it not. In a dream, in a vision of the night, when deep sleep falleth upon men, in slumberings upon the bed; Then he openeth the ears of men, and sealeth their instruction." (Job 33:14-16).

67. In ancient Greece, the Great Mother was known as the Queen Bee, and her priestess was Melissa, or the bee. The honey bee was a sacred symbol of Artemis and a prominent design on Ephesian coins for almost 600 years.

Mythology tells us that the lips of the poets were touched by bees, or the "birds of the muses." Sophocles and Plato are said to have had their lips anointed with honey as babies, and Achilles and Pythagoras were fed honey as infants.

68. The Achaemenid Empire, also called the First Persian Empire, was founded by Cyrus the Great. Ranging at its greatest extent from Eastern Europe to the Indus Valley, it was larger than any previous empire in history, spanning 5.5 million square kilometers.

69. "May the Force be with you!" declared General Dodonna, before the Death Star battle in Episode 4 of the Star Wars saga. Obi-Wan Kenobe described the Force as "what gives a Jedi his power. It is an energy field created by all living things. It surrounds us and penetrates us. It binds the galaxy together."

Duct tape, something with which we are all familiar, is like the Force. It has a light side, and a dark side, and it, too, binds the universe together.

The Master Teacher Yoda explained to young Luke Skywalker: "A Jedi's strength flows from the Force. But beware of the dark side: Anger, fear, and aggression. The dark side are they. Easily they flow, quick to join you in a fight. If once you start down

260

the dark path, forever will it dominate your destiny, consume you it will." We must resist the temptation to yield to the dark side, or to the baser elements of our nature.

70. A shamal is a northwesterly wind blowing over the Persian Gulf, occurring several times a year, but mostly in the summer months. It can create large sandstorms.

71. "The wind bloweth where it listeth, and thou hearest the sound thereof, but canst not tell whence it cometh and whither it goeth. So is every one that is born of the Spirit." (John 3:8).

72. "Seek ye the Lord while he may be found. Call upon him while he is near." (Isaiah 55:6).

73. "The kingdom of heaven is like unto a merchant man, seeking goodly pearls." (Matthew 23:45).

74. "Happy is the man that findeth wisdom, and the man that getteth understanding. For the merchandise of it is better than the merchandise of silver, and the gain thereof than fine gold. She is more precious than rubies." (Proverbs 3:13-15).

"Thou has been in Eden, the garden of God; every precious stone was thy covering, the sardius, topaz, and the diamond, the beryl, the onyx, and the jasper, the sapphire, the emerald, and the carbuncle, and gold: the workmanship of thy tabrets and of thy pipes was prepared in thee in the day that thou wast created." (Ezekiel 28:13).

75. "Adam spake, as he was moved upon by the Holy Ghost, and a genealogy was kept of the children of God. And this was the book of the generations of Adam." (Moses 6:8).

76. See Proverbs 2:2.

77. Modern historians identify Sheba with the South Arabian kingdom of Saba, in present-day Yemen.

78. "I found a woman ruling them, and she has been given of all things, and she has a great throne. I found her and her people prostrating to the sun instead of Allah, and Satan has made their deeds pleasing to them and averted them from (His) way, so they are not guided." (Qu'ran 27:23-24).

79. The Seven Wonders of the Ancient World were remarkable constructions. Of the originals, only one remains relatively intact, the Great Pyramid of Giza, which also happens to be the oldest of the seven.

80. The Al-Aqsa Mosque, in the Old City of Jerusalem, is the third holiest site in Islam. It lies atop the Temple Mount, known as the Al Asqa Compound among Muslims. They believe that Mohammed was transported from the Great Mosque of Mecca to Al-Aqsa during the Night Journey, and that he led prayers from there until Allah directed him to turn toward the Kaaba, in Mecca.

81. Jerusalem is located on a plateau in the Judaean Mountains between the Mediterranean and the Dead Sea. It is one of the oldest cities in the world and is considered holy to the three major Abrahamic religions of Judaism, Christianity, and Islam.

82. The Kaaba (Cube), also referred to as al-Ka'bah al-Musharrafah (Honorable Kaaba), is a building at the center of Islam's most important mosque, the Great Mosque of Mecca. It is the most sacred site in Islam, considered by Muslims to be the House of God. Its location determines the direction Muslims face when kneeling in prayer, wherever in the world they may be. Muslims are expected to face the Kaaba when performing the Salah, the five daily Islamic prayers.

264

One of the Five Pillars of Islam requires every Muslim who is able to do so to perform the Hajj (Pilgrimage) to Mecca, at least once in their lifetime.

83. Mecca is the birthplace of Mohammed. A cave there was the site of Mohammed's first revelation of the Quran or Koran, and a pilgrimage to it, known as the Hajj, is obligatory for all able Muslims. Mecca is home to the Kaaba, one of Islam's holiest sites and is the orientation of Muslim prayer. Thus, Mecca is regarded as the holiest city in Islam.

84. Prophets in Islam are individuals who were sent by God to various communities in order to serve as examples of ideal human behavior and to spread God's message on earth. Sometimes, they transmit divine revelation through the intercession of angels.

Muslims believe that many prophets have been sent by Allah, including many not mentioned in the Quran, or Koran. The Quran states: "There is a messenger for every community". Belief in the Islamic prophets is one of the six articles of faith of Islam.

85. Al-Masjid an-Nabawi is a mosque established and built by the Islamic prophet Mohammed, situated in the city of Medina in the Hejaz region of Saudi Arabia. It was one of the first mosques built by Mohammed, and is now one of the largest mosques in the world.

86. Medina is the capital of the Al-Madinah Region in Saudi Arabia. At the city's heart is al-Masjid an-Nabawi, which is the burial place of the Islamic prophet, Mohammed. Medina is one of the three holiest cities in Islam, the other two being Mecca and Jerusalem.

87. "Usually angels are not seen. Sometimes they are. But, seen or

unseen, they are always near. Sometimes, their assignments are grand and have significance for the whole world. Sometimes, the messages are private. Occasionally, the angelic purpose is to warn. But most often, it is to comfort, to provide merciful attention or guidance in difficult times." (Jeffrey R. Holland).

88. "It was not a voice of thunder, neither was it a voice of a great tumultuous noise, but behold, it was a still voice of perfect mildness, as if it had been a whisper, and it did pierce even to the very soul." (Helaman 5:30).

"Thus saith the still small voice, which whispereth through and pierceth all things, and often times it maketh my bones to quake while it maketh manifest." (D&C 85:6).

"Then the king's countenance was changed, and his thoughts troubled him, so that the joints his loins were loosed, and his knees smote one against another." (Daniel 5:6).

89. "Where there is no vision, the people perish." (Proverbs 29:18).

90. The Arabian Desert occupies almost the entire Arabian Peninsula, and is the largest desert on the continent of Asia (900,000 square miles). It is the second largest desert on earth, surpassed only by the Sahara, in northern Africa. Rainfall averages less than 4 inches (100 mm) a year but can range from 0 to 20 inches (0 to 500 mm).

91. Drylands around the Arabian Peninsula are the main terrestrial sources of airborne dust. Sandstorms can be up to 100 kilometers wide and several kilometers high. The Persian ruler Cambyses II conquered Egypt in the sixth century B.C.E. According to the Greek historian Herodotus, his army of 50,000 then set out for the Siwa Oasis. As legend has it, his army then vanished, buried by a dust storm.

268

92. "Time is the fire in which we burn." (Delmore Schwartz, "Calmly We Walk Through This April's Day" from his collection titled "In Dreams Begin Responsibilities").

93. The universe is a well-knit, formally created structure in which there are no gaps, no dislocations, and no ruptures. It is an extraordinarily well-built machine, which works according to the laws that God has put into it. The Koran, therefore, calls the universe and everything in it Muslim, which is translated 'surrender to God's law or to God's will.' Because the universe obeys His laws that are engrained in it, the Koran frequently calls the whole universe Muslim. Man is invited to be Muslim. Whereas the rest of the universe automatically obeys God, man has been given the choice to obey or disobey." ("Elements of Belief" in "The Koran, Literature of Belief," p. 82-83).

94. "The word qur'an means a reading or discourse, and is applied by Muslims to the whole, or to any section, of their sacred scriptures. The Koran is an accumulation, and orthodoxy claims it to be in every syllable inspired by God. It is the work of one man, the Prophet Mohammed, and is therefore without question the most influential book ever produced by a single hand." (Will Durant, "The Lessons of History," Volume 4, page 175).

95. "Though I speak with the tongues of men and of angels, and have not charity, I am become as sounding brass, or a tinkling cymbal." (1 Corinthians 13:1).

96. "Some men see things as they are, and ask why. I dream of things that never were, and ask why not." (W. Somerset Maugham).

97. "Time and tide wait for no man." (Geoffrey Chaucer). This proverbial phrase, alluding to the fact that human events or concerns cannot stop the passage of time or the movement of

the tides, first appeared about 1395 C.E. in Chaucer's Prologue to the Clerk's Tale.

98. Attributed to Omar Khayyam.

99. The Rubiat of Omar Khayyam.

100. The idea of a last will and testament is one that dates back to ancient Rome, but the laws governing wills in the United States arose out of English common law. The principle that guides the concept of wills, is that one has certain property rights in both land and personal possessions. Since death is inevitable, even ancient cultures recognized the need to provide for a means by which individuals could name, in writing, the beneficiaries of their worldly possessions.

101. Zakat is a form of alms-giving considered by Islam to be a religious obligation or tax, which is next after prayer in importance. As one of the Five Pillars of Islam, zakat is a religious duty for all Muslims who meet the necessary criteria of wealth.

102. The ritual obligations of Islam are called the Five Pillars. They are acknowledged and practiced by Muslims throughout the world. They are viewed as compulsory for individuals who genuinely wish to emulate Mohammad. The pillars are shahada, a profession of faith, salat, or prayer, zakat, or almsgiving, sawm, or fasting, and hajj, or pilgrimage.

103. "Righteousness is not that ye turn your faces to the East or to the West, but righteousness is this: whosoever believeth in God, and the Last Day, and the angels, and the Book, and the Prophets; and whosoever, for the love of God, giveth of his wealth unto his kindred, unto orphans, and the poor, and the wayfarer, and to the beggar, and for the release of captives; and whoso observeth prayer, and, when they have covenanted, fulfill

272

their covenant; and who are patient in adversity and hardship and in the times of violence: these are the righteous, these are they who believe in the Lord! (Koran, ii, 177).

104. Dervish in Islam refers broadly to members of a Sufi fraternity who choose or accept material poverty, found particularly in Persian communities.

105. Mujahid is a Muslim who is engaged in what is considered to be a jihad, a struggle, or holy war.

106. Jihad is an Arabic word that can literally mean "striving or struggling," especially with a praiseworthy aim. In an Islamic context, it can refer to almost any effort to make life conform to God's guidance, such as proselytizing, efforts toward the moral betterment of the ummah (or community), or the struggle against evil inclinations. Currently, it is most frequently associated with holy war.

107. The Arabian or Arab horse is a breed that originated on the Arabian Peninsula. With a distinctive head shape and high tail carriage, the Arabian is one of the most easily recognizable breeds in the world.

108. The Pool of Shifa' alludes to the Book of Healing, which was an encyclopedia written by Abu Ali ibn Sina, in medieval Persia. In spite of its title, The Book of Healing is not focused on medicine. Shifa' is intended to cure ignorance of the soul, through recovery, recuperation, and restoration.

109. The west wind is the awakener of the Mediterranean Sea, lulled to sleep by its own currents and seeing in its slumber "old palaces and towers ... overgrown with azure moss and flowers." (Percy Bysshe Shelly, "Ode to the West Wind.")

110. "If one looked very carefully, sewn onto the cushion upon

which the glass slippers rested, was the word that Cinderella and the prince found to be even greater than magic. It was more than dreams, more than hope, and even more than happily ever after. It was love." ("Cinderella – The Rest of The Story").

About The Author

Phil Hudson and his wife Jan have 7 children and over 25 grandchildren. They enjoy spending time with their family at their cabin nestled in the Selkirk Mountains, on the shore of Priest Lake, the crown jewel of North Idaho. Phil had a successful dental practice in Spokane, Washington for 43 years, before retiring in 2015. He has an eclectic mix of hobbies, and enjoys the out of doors. He always finds time, however, to record his thoughts on his laptop, and understands Isaac Asimov's response when he was asked: If you knew that you had only 10 minutes left to live, what would you do?" He answered: "I'd type faster."

Phil received the inspiration to write this book while he and Jan were serving as missionaries for The Church of Jesus Christ of Latter-day Saints, in the Kingdom of Tonga. While there, they celebrated their 50th wedding anniversary.

By The Author

Essays

      Volume One: Spray From The Ocean Of Thought
      Volume Two: Ripples On A Pond
      Volume Three: Serendipitous Meanderings
      Volume Four: Presents Of Mind
      Volume Five: Mental Floss
      Volume Six: Fitness Training For The Mind And Spirit

First Principles and Ordinances Series

      Faith - Our Hearts Are Changed
      Repentance - A Broken Heart and a Contrite Spirit
      Baptism - One Hundred And One Reasons Why We Are Baptized
      The Holy Ghost - That We Might Have His Spirit To Be With Us
      The Sacrament - This Do In Remembrance Of Me

Book of Mormon Commentary

      Volume One: Born In The Wilderness
      Volume Two: Voices From The Dust
      Volume Three: Journey To Cumorah

Doctrine & Covenants Commentary

Volume One - Sections 1 - 34
Volume Two - Sections 35 - 57

Minute Musings: Spontaneous Combustions of Thought

Volume One
Volume Two
Volume Three

Calendars:

As I Think About The Savior
In His Own Words: Discovering William Tyndale
Scriptural Symbols

Children & Youth

Book of Mormon Hiking Song
Happy Birthday
Muddy, Muddy
The Hiawatha Trail: An Allegory
The Little Princess
The Parable of The Pencil
The Thirteen Articles of Faith

Doctrinal Themes

Are Christians Mormon? Volume One
Are Christians Mormon? Volume One
Christmas is The Season When...
Dentistry in The Scriptures
Gratitude
Hebrew Poetry
Hiding in Plain Sight
One Hundred Questions Answered by The Book of Mormon
The Highways and Byways of Life
The House of The Lord
The Parable of The Pencil
Without The Book of Mormon
Writing on Metal Plates

A Thought For Each Day of the Year

Baptism
Faith
Life's Greatest Questions
Repentance
Revelation
The Atonement
The Holy Ghost
The House of the Lord
The Plan of Salvation
The Sabbath
The Sacrament

Professional Publications

Diode Laser Soft Tissue Surgery Volume One
Diode Laser Soft Tissue Surgery Volume Two
Diode Laser Soft Tissue Surgery Volume Three

These, and other titles, are available from online retailers.

Quid magis
possum dicere?

CPSIA information can be obtained
at www.ICGtesting.com
Printed in the USA
LVHW061814150722
723592LV00010B/239

9 781950 647507